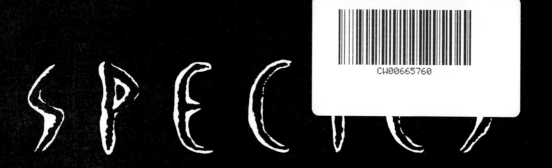

SPECIES™

BOXTREE

Rachelle Menashe
Colourist

Dennis Feldman
Writer

John Bolton
Cover Artist

Jon Foster
Pencils

Robert V Conte
Series Editor

Brian Kane
Inks

Scott Fuentes
Series Designer

Pat Brosseau
Lettering

First published in Great Britain in 1995 by Boxtree Limited,
Broadwall House, 21 Broadwall, London SE1 9PL

10 9 8 7 6 5 4 3 2 1

ISBN: 0 7522 0762 8

Printed and bound in Great Britain by Cambus Litho, East Kilbride. A CIP catalogue
entry for this book is available from the British Library.

ARECIBO, 1992...

S-E-
There's someone out there for you.

Search for Extra-Terrestrial Intelligence:
Long-distance relationships can work.

MAN, WHEN'S THE ALIEN GONNA TAKE OVER THE EARTH IN THIS COMIC--

BEEP!

BEEP!

JEEZ, NOT ANOTHER ONE...

KLIK!

EH--?

HOLY SHIT!

SETI HEAD-QUARTERS...

MY GOD, A MESSAGE...

LANGLEY, VIRGINIA. C.I.A. HEADQUARTERS. CRYPTOGRAPHERS' ROOM -- BASEMENT...

JESUS...

LET ME REVIEW WHAT WE KNOW...

...THE MESSAGE WAS IN TWO *DISTINCT* SEGMENTS. IT CAME WITH A DICTIONARY THAT WAS VIRTUALLY SELF-DECIPHERING...

XAVIER FITCH, PROJECT DIRECTOR -- OPERATION DISTANT CALL.

...WE'VE DECODED THE FIRST SEGMENT, A *CATALYST* FOR METHANE. WE NOW HAVE A CLEAN-BURNING FUEL AT *ONE HUNDREDTH* THE PRICE IT FORMERLY COST.

THE SECOND IS THE INTERESTING ONE... THEY'RE ASKING US TO COMBINE THEIR DNA WITH OURS IN A *HUMAN CELL.*

WHY WOULD THEY DO THAT?

THEY WANT US TO BUILD SOMETHING THAT CAN SURVIVE HERE ON EARTH AND SPEAK WITH US.

IT MAY BE GENETICALLY PROGRAMMED TO CARRY THEIR MESSAGE, PERHAPS EVEN EXPAND ON IT. A *WET MACHINE.*

WHERE DID THIS MESSAGE ORIGINATE?

WE CAN'T TELL. IT APPEARS TO HAVE BEEN PULLED AROUND A SERIES OF *BLACK HOLES.* WE CAN'T EVEN TELL WHICH DIRECTION IT CAME FROM.

AND YOU WANT US TO BLINDLY BUILD SOMETHING LIKE THAT?

THIS MESSAGE MAY HAVE BEEN RECEIVED BY CHINA, JAPAN, RUSSIA... ARE WE PREPARED TO TAKE THE CHANCE WE'LL BE THE ONES THAT *DON'T KNOW* WHAT THEY HAVE TO TELL US?

WHY DO THEY NEED *OUR* DNA?

IT'S A MAP FOR *SURVIVING* ON EARTH. IF THEY TAKE OUR SHAPE AND FORM, THEY'LL BE ABLE TO BREATHE THIS ATMOSPHERE, RESIST THIS GRAVITY, AND MAINTAIN A WORKABLE TEMPERATURE.

WE'RE WHAT'S *THRIVED* ON THIS PLANET, SO THEY WANT THEIR MESSENGER TO BE LIKE US.

THEY'VE THOUGHT OF EVERYTHING, HAVEN'T THEY?

PROBABLY *MORE* THAN WE CAN UNDERSTAND.

A HUNDRED HUMAN OVUM ARE INJECTED WITH ALIEN DNA.

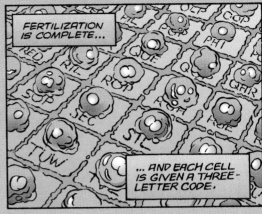

FERTILIZATION IS COMPLETE...

... AND EACH CELL IS GIVEN A THREE-LETTER CODE.

SEVEN DIVIDE. FOUR PETER OUT.

TWO ARE REMOVED AND STORED IN LIQUID NITROGEN.

ONE IS ALLOWED TO GROW...

THIS IS AMAZING-- IT'S ONLY BEEN TWO DAYS!

THEN WE BETTER PREPARE A WAY TO CONTROL AND ISOLATE IT-- SOON!

GET...
AWAY...

PREDATION:
THE FIRST
GREAT THEME
OF NATURE.

CRACKLE!

GET...

...AWAY!

PANT!
PANT!

GASP--!

SIL REACTS INSTINCTIVELY...

THWAPP!

CRUNCH!

URN

...AND FATALLY!

MORNING...

THERE WERE ONLY A FEW TRAINS LAST NIGHT. THINK SHE COULD HAVE GOTTEN THIS FAR?

IS SHE THAT *FAST*?

SHE'S *THAT* FAST.

ATTENTION... THE *FOOD SERVICE CAR* IS CLOSED UNTIL WE REACH *LAS VEGAS*--

HAVE CLOTHES...

--ALL *NEW* PASSENGERS, PLEASE HAVE YOUR TICKETS READY...

SHELTER...

MONEY...

KRAKK!

AND *FOOD*...

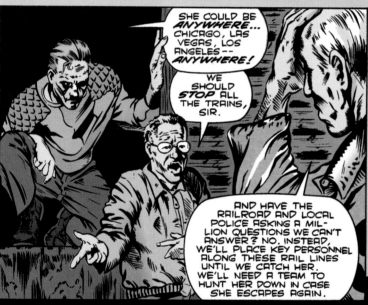

PART TWO
THE CHRYSALIS

THE HEAD OF THE *DISTANT CALL* PROJECT, *XAVIER FITCH,* CHECKS HIS FILES...

I'LL NEED PEOPLE WITH THE RIGHT COMBINATION OF *SKILLS* TO HUNT DOWN SIL...

...A *CROSS-CULTURAL EXPERT* TO TELL US HOW SHE'LL ADAPT TO OUR SOCIETY...

DR. STEPHEN ARDEN, PROFESSOR OF ANTHROPOLO-GY, HARVARD UNIVERSITY.

...A *BIOLOGIST* TO TELL US ABOUT HER ANIMAL IN-STINCTS...

DR. LAURA BAKER, GENETICIST.

...AN *EMPATH* TO TELL US WHAT SHE'S FEELING...

DAN SMITHSON, EMPATH.

...AND A *HUNTER,* TO MAKE SURE SHE DOESN'T GET AWAY.

PRESTON LENNOX, OCCUPATION CLASSIFIED.

SIL'S METAMORPHOSIS IS *COMPLETE*...

ATTENTION, PASSENGERS-- WE HAVE ARRIVED AT OUR FINAL STOP, LOS ANGELES. PLEASE MAKE SURE TO REMOVE ALL PERSONAL BELONGINGS BEFORE DEPARTING. THANK YOU.

NO THIS ISN'T *HER!*

FREEDOM...

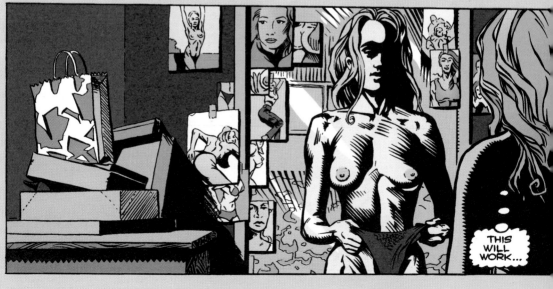

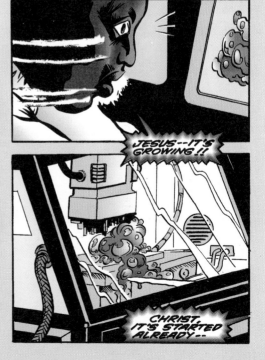

UGHNN...

HISSSS

COME ON!

SLAM!

KUK

DECEPTION -- ONE OF NATURE'S MOST COMMON DEFENSES.

:HUFF-PUFF!:

I HOPE YOU UNDERSTAND I HAD NO *CHOICE* BUT TO FOLLOW PROTOCOL.

RIGHT...

MEANWHILE, SIL PURSUES HER INSTINCTS...

HEY, YOU FROM AROUND HERE?

NO, I'M... *FOREIGN*--

HEY, SEXY... I'VE GOT A PARTY TO GO TO, AND *NO ONE* TO TAKE ME.

I'LL TAKE YOU.

GOOD. I'LL BE RIGHT BACK. GOT TO GO TO THE *LITTLE GIRLS' ROOM.*

SIL IS OUT-COMPETED...

WASH *BLOOD*...

...WITH THE ARMY ASSISTING US, SIL CAN'T *ESCAPE*.

JESUS...

...I'VE SEEN SOME CRAZY STUFF IN MY TIME...

...BUT THIS IS TOTALLY *INSANE*.

SHOWER'S RUNNING...

STTTTTTTTTT

DAMN, THERE'S NOTHING. NOTHING AT ALL.

IT'S OBVIOUS, FITCH--SHE'S TRYING TO *REPRODUCE*.

WHAT WAS SHE DOING *HERE*?

SHE HAD *SEX* WITH HIM?

I DON'T THINK SO, ARDEN.

HOW CAN YOU TELL, PRESS?

HE STILL HAS HIS PANTS *ON*.

GOOD POINT, BUT WHY *DIDN'T* THEY MATE?

SHE PROBABLY REJECTED HIM.

REJECTED HIM?!

IT'S POSSIBLE HE HAD A *DISEASE*, OR *GENETIC DEFECTS* THAT WOULD MAKE HIM AN UNACCEPTABLE CHOICE.

HOW WOULD SHE KNOW THAT?

SPECIAL SENSES. RATS CAN SENSE DISEASE OR GENETIC DAMAGE IN POTENTIAL MATES.

WAIT...

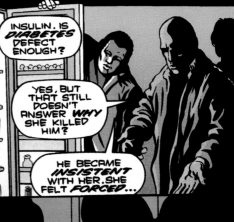

INSULIN. IS *DIABETES* DEFECT ENOUGH?

YES, BUT THAT STILL DOESN'T ANSWER *WHY* SHE KILLED HIM?

HE BECAME *INSISTENT* WITH HER. SHE FELT *FORCED*...

WHERE DO YOU THINK SHE IS NOW, DAN?

PROBABLY A PLACE WHERE SHE CAN BE *ALONE*.

THIS IS WHAT HAPPENED IN *AMERICA*, NOT TOO LONG AGO...

cLiK

NO, PRESS, THE *AMERICAN INDIANS*.

THE EXTINCTION OF THE *BUFFALO*?

EXACTLY, ARDEN--

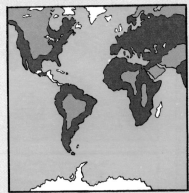

--NOW HERE'S *OUR* PROBLEM...

WHERE ARE WE?

WE'RE THE GREEN.

THAT'S THE *POINT*.

THERE IS *NO* GREEN.

MEANWHILE, SIL LEARNS A HARD LESSON OF THE ROAD...

WHAT'S... WRONG WITH THIS CAR?

RRRRRRR

WHERE SHOULD I GO?

HA-HAAAA, I'LL CROSS THIS HIGHWAY IN NO TIME--

KLA

HEY, LADY-- LOOK OUT!

--FLAT--

WHUMP!

WHA--?

SKREECH

...CAN'T BELIEVE I *HIT* SOME-- HUH?!

YOU'RE ALL RIGHT--?!

YES.

THE DOCTOR SAID IT WAS OKAY FOR YOU TO LEAVE?

YES.

...I'M GLAD YOU CAME HERE WITH ME. I LOVE BEING AWAY FROM THE CITY.

LET'S M MORTAL THE MOME SHALL WE

THHH·KC

...A DOCTOR REPORTED SOMETHING *STRANGE* AT THE EMERGENCY ROOM UP THE HIGHWAY. PRESS, LAURA -- CHECK IT OUT.

RIGHT.

...MAYBE I'M WORKING TOO HARD, BUT I HAVE ABSOLUTELY NO WAY OF *EXPLAINING* WHAT I SAW.

DID YOU TAKE A BLOOD SAMPLE?

SURE DID.

IT'S HER!

WATER'S NICE. COME ON IN.

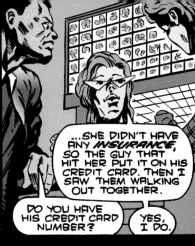

...SHE DIDN'T HAVE ANY *INSURANCE*, SO THE GUY THAT HIT HER PUT IT ON HIS CREDIT CARD. THEN I SAW THEM WALKING OUT TOGETHER.

DO YOU HAVE HIS CREDIT CARD NUMBER?

YES, I DO.

YOU'VE BEEN... *KIND* TO ME... NOT MANY PEOPLE HAVE ... I *LIKE* YOU.

I LIKE YOU, TOO.

...IT'S AN ADDRESS IN THE *PALISADES*. WE'D BETTER HEAD WEST.

SCREEEEE

GET FITCH ON THE PHONE AND TELL HIM WHERE WE'RE GOING.

KISS ME...

I DON'T THINK IT'S TOO SOON, DO YOU?

NO. IT'S JUST... *RIGHT*.

THIS GUY AIN'T GONNA LIKE IT WHEN WE TELL HIM HE'S ABOUT TO *MAKE IT* WITH A *MONSTER*. HEH-HEH.

HEY, I'M OVER *HERE*, DOLL.

I...*HEAR* SOMEONE...

KLIK-KLAK

LET'S GO AROUND THE *SIDE*...

YOU'RE RIGHT. I HEAR SOMEONE, TOO. I'LL CHECK IT OUT--

DON'T GO. STAY...

HEY! WHAT ARE YOU--

TAP-TAP

YES...

RRRRR

MUST ESCAPE...

BA-BOOM!

LOOKS LIKE THE HELICOPTERS'LL ENSURE WE WON'T FIND ANY *REMAINS.*

DON'T YOU THINK THAT'S BETTER THAN HAVING *ANY* OF HER SURVIVE?

...WHILE THERE'S TIME...

...I DON'T BUY IT. SIL'S BEEN AHEAD OF US EVERY STEP OF THE WAY.

WELL, WE FOUND WHAT LOOKS LIKE A THUMB ENTANGLED IN THE CAR DOOR THAT BROKE OFF.

LET'S CHECK IT TO ENSURE IT'S A GENETIC MATCH.

IT WILL BE. WE GOT HER.

THIS CHANGE WILL DECEIVE THEM...

...THE CORONER'S CONFIRMED THE THUMB'S A MATCH. SIL IS DEAD. CONGRATULATIONS, IT'S BEEN A PLEASURE WORKING WITH ALL OF YOU.

WHY DO I THINK FITCH DOESN'T MEAN WHAT HE SAID...

LET'S GET SOME REST. COMING, PRESS?

NAH, I'M GONNA READ A WHILE. I'LL SEE YOU TOMORROW.

LATER...

...SOMETHING'S REALLY WEIRD...

WHAT FLOOR?

UM, TEN.

THINKING HER CHILD IS SAFE, SIL HUNTS HER REMAINING PURSUERS--

--ONE BY ONE!

UGGNNN

MY GOD... LAURA, THERE'S A CHILD UP HERE!

STAY AWAY FROM IT, DAN!

SIL WATCHES HER CHILD'S LIFELESS REMAINS BURN TO ASHES AS SHE IS OVERCOME BY A BURNING DESIRE FOR *REVENGE...*

HOWEVER--

DIE, YOU MOTHER-FUCKER!

BLAMM!

LATER...

...SIL WAS HALF US, HALF SOMETHING ELSE.

WHICH DO YOU THINK WAS THE *PREDATORY* HALF, HERS OR OURS?

I DON'T KNOW... LAURA, WHAT BEAUTIFUL *EYES* YOU HAVE...

"...AND IN *FRONT,* TOO."

SQUEEEK-SQUEEK-SQU~

THWAAP!

POP!

THE FIRST GREAT THEME OF NATURE: *PREDATION.*

SQUARKK!

IT'S NOT OVER...

SPECIES ™

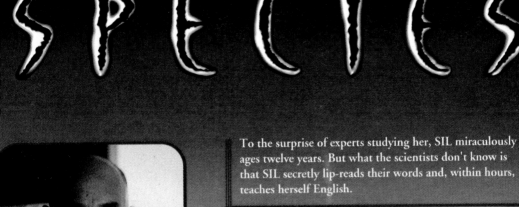

To the surprise of experts studying her, SIL miraculously ages twelve years. But what the scientists don't know is that SIL secretly lip-reads their words and, within hours, teaches herself English.

Project director Xavier Fitch (played by Ben Kingsley) heads Operation Distant Call, the scientific experiment that creates the alien/human hybrid named SIL.

After SIL's first nightmare causes some momentary (but shocking) physical changes, lab technicians are ordered to release deadly cyanide gas into her holding cell. However, SIL knows what they're up to . . .

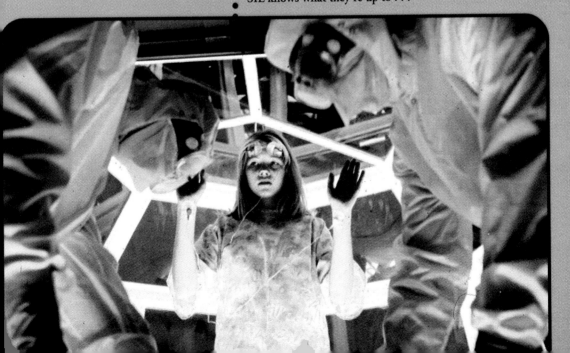

. . . and quickly escapes to freedom.

Unfortunately, many scientists and technicians aren't so lucky and succumb to poisonous fumes that pollute the lab area.

Shortly after SIL's escape into the outside world, Fitch sends a massive search party to hunt her down.

SIL quickly boards a train en route to Las Vegas and kills a hobo to take his clothing.

After transferring to a train bound for Los Angeles, SIL takes time to learn some of earth's technology. She is especially fascinated by a portable television set.

GRAPHIC NOVELS

ALIENS
- ☐ 0 7522 0878 0   Aliens v Preator – Deadliest of the Species 1   £9.99 pb
- ☐ 0 7522 0695 8   Aliens v Preator – Deadliest of the Species 2   £9.99 pb

RANMA
- ☐ 0 7522 0851 9   Ranma Book 1   £5.99 pb
- ☐ 0 7522 0861 6   Ranma Book 2   £5.99 pb

SPIDER-MAN
- ☐ 0 7522 0107 7   Masques   £8.99 pb
- ☐ 0 7522 0112 3   Perceptions   £8.99 pb
- ☐ 0 7522 0876 4   The Return of the Sinister 6   £9.99 pb
- ☐ 0 7522 0808 X   Revenge of the Sinister 6   £7.99 pb

STAR WARS
- ☐ 0 7522 0893 4   Classic – A New Hope   £8.99 pb
- ☐ 0 7522 0987 6   Dark Empire   £9.99 pb
- ☐ 0 7522 0822 5   Dark Empire 2   £9.99 pb
- ☐ 0 7522 0793 8   Dark Empire/Epilogue   £6.99 pb
- ☐ 0 7522 0616 8   Dark Lords of Sith 1   £8.99 pb
- ☐ 0 7522 0804 7   Droids   £8.99 pb
- ☐ 0 7522 0606 0   Empire Strikes Back   £7.99 pb
- ☐ 0 7522 0704 0   Jabba the Hutt   £8.99 pb
- ☐ 0 7522 0611 7   Return of the Jedi   £7.99 pb
- ☐ 0 7522 0798 9   River of Chaos   £8.99 pb
- ☐ 0 7522 0913 2   Star Wars Classic   £7.99 pb
- ☐ 0 7522 0747 4   Star Wars Classic 2   £9.99 pb
- ☐ 0 7522 0752 0   Star Wars Classic 3   £9.99 pb
- ☐ 0 7522 0817 9   Tales of the Jedi and Freedom Nadd Uprising   £10.99 pb

STAR TREK – DEEP SPACE NINE
- ☐ 0 7522 0928 0   Emancipation 1   £7.99 pb
- ☐ 0 7522 0933 7   Emancipation and Beyond   £7.99 pb
- ☐ 0 7522 0898 5   Hearts and Minds   £7.99 pb
- ☐ 0 7522 0888 8   Requiem   £7.99 pb

STREETFIGHTER
- ☐ 0 7522 0813 6   Street Fighter II – book 1   £6.99 pb
- ☐ 0 7522 0818 7   Street Fighter II – book 2   £6.99 pb

VARIOUS
- ☐ 0 7522 0897 7   Daredevil – man without fear   £9.99 pb
- ☐ 0 7522 0962 0   Necroscope   £7.99 pb
- ☐ 0 7522 0645 1   Marvels   £10.99 pb
- ☐ 0 7522 0881 0   Mask (film tie-in)   £6.99 pb
- ☐ 0 7522 0977 9   RoboCop: Prime Suspect   £7.99 pb
- ☐ 0 7522 0856 X   Shadow (film tie-in)   £6.99 pb
- ☐ 0 7522 0762 8   Species Movie (tie-in)   £8.99 pb

X MEN
- ☐ 0 7522 0892 6   Adventures   £9.99 pb
- ☐ 1 85283 390 4   Brood Trouble In The Big Easy   £5.25 pb
- ☐ 1 85283 394 7   Essential Guide   £9.99 pb
- ☐ 0 7522 0756 3   Gambit   £7.99 pb
- ☐ 0 7522 0691 5   Ghostrider/Wolverine/Punisher/Hearts of Darkness/Dark Design   £7.99 pb
- ☐ 0 7522 0871 3   God Loves, Man Kills   £5.99 pb
- ☐ 0 7522 0103 4   Rogue   £8.99 pb
- ☐ 0 7522 0803 9   Sabretooth   £6.99 pb
- ☐ 1 85283 395 5   Wolverine   £6.99 pb
- ☐ 0 7522 0108 5   Wolverine – Triumph and Tragedy   £9.99 pb
- ☐ 0 7522 0151 4   Uncanny X-Men: Acts of Vengeance   £8.99 pb
- ☐ 0 7522 0161 1   Uncanny X-Men: Wolverine/Psylocke 1   £8.99 pb

All these books are available at your local bookshop or can be ordered direct from the publisher. Just tick the titles you want and fill in the form below.

Prices and availability subject to change without notice.

Boxtree Cash Sales, P.O. Box 11, Falmouth, Cornwall TR10 9EN

Please send a cheque or postal order for the value of the book and add the following for postage and packing:

U.K. including B.F.P.O. – £1.00 for one book plus 50p for the second book, and 30p for each additional book ordered up to a £3.00 maximum.

Overseas including Eire – £2.00 for the first book plus £1.00 for the second book, and 50p for each additional book ordered.

OR please debit this amount from my Access/Visa Card (delete as appropriate).

Card Number   ☐☐☐☐ ☐☐☐☐ ☐☐☐☐ ☐☐☐☐ ☐☐☐☐

Amount £ ....

Expiry Date ....

Signed ....

Name ....

Address ....